Knight Training

Written by Lisa Thompson
Pictures by Andy Hamilton

Arthur wanted to be a knight.

On Monday, Eric the Knight said, "Time to wash the horse."

So Arthur washed the horse.

3

On Tuesday, Eric the Knight said, "Time to go riding."

Arthur thought riding would be fun.

He was wrong!

Wednesday was fighting day.

Arthur tried to fight Eric the Knight, but Eric was too good.

7

On Thursday, Eric the Knight said, "A knight needs to know how to shoot an arrow."

Shooting arrows was not fun!

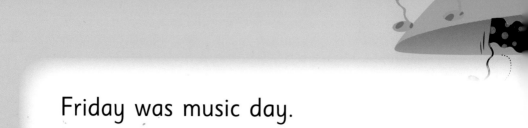

Friday was music day.

Eric the Knight showed Arthur how to sing.

Arthur did not like his singing at all.

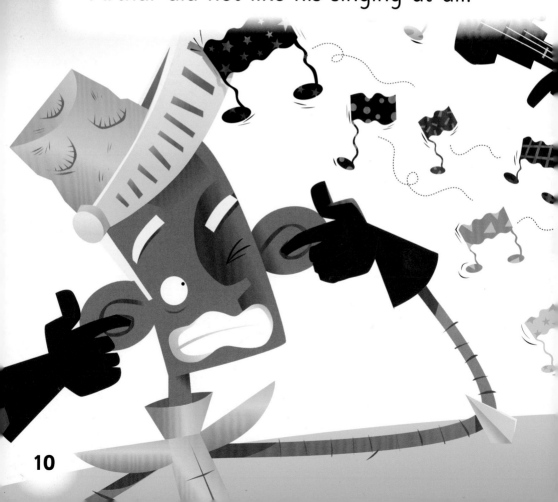

On Saturday, Eric the Knight said,
"A knight needs to know how to play chess.

Eric always won.

But on Sunday, *Arthur* said, "Today is fun day. I am good at having fun!"

15

Think About!

What was the most fun activity that Arthur had to do?

How could Arthur become better at each activity?

Have you had to work very hard at doing something?